Sometimes I
Running Riley's Story.

This book belongs to:

This is your book. Draw in it. Doodle over it. Write within it. Colour in the lines or go over them. It's up to you.

Let your imagination run through the pages.

Published by
B3long
Suite 78, 123 Stratford Road,
Shirley, Solihull.
B90 3ND
www.b3long.co.uk

Text copyright F Newood 2016
Illustrations copyright G Newood 2016
First Published 2016

ISBN: 978-0-9926629-1-2

This book is dedicated to all the adults who
walk beside all the children who want to run.

We thank you.

Sometimes I Run.

Running Riley's Story.

What happens in Running Riley's brain
when he feels unsafe.

Written by Fi Newood
Illustrated by Gail Newood

Sometimes when my feelings seem to big for me to handle, I run.

I run hard and fast.

My legs pound the ground, my heart races

and my breathing gets quicker.

I run until I can't run anymore.

Sometimes I run and I don't know where I am running to.

I just run and run and run.

Sometimes I run in search of something but I don't know what until I find it.

Usually it's a hiding place,

somewhere that I can rest until my body calms down.

Sometimes I can't run.

Sometimes my body feels frozen or there's no way for me to escape.

It's then that I run inside my head in dreams that I create to make me feel safe and happy.

Sometimes, when the running is over, I realise that I have run far away from the people that help me to be safe and I don't always know how to get back to them.

Sometimes I realise that in my hurry to run away I have hurt people or I have hurt myself.

I don't mean to but then I worry that I will get in trouble for not keeping everyone safe.

I used to think that all this running was something that only I did.

But then this one time I read in a book that all people find that when feelings get too much they want to run sometimes.

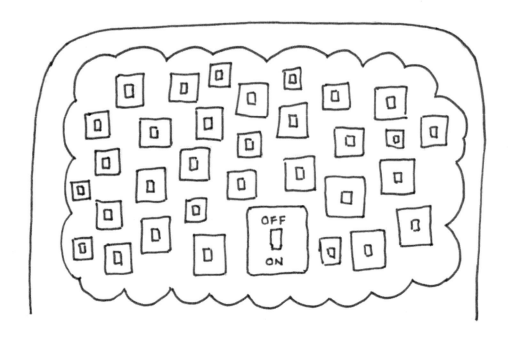

It's because our brains are
created this way.

Of all the millions and millions of
switches inside our head
the biggest switch is the safety
switch and when we feel scared it
can make us want to run.

Sometimes I know when I start to feel unsafe because I can feel it building inside of me.

Sometimes there is no warning sign, something happens, my safety switch suddenly turns on and I just have to run.

Sometimes when I've been
running I feel bad

and wish I had spoken to an adult who helps me manage my switches.

But I'm working on that.

Now you have read Running Riley's story, why don't you think about how you can keep yourself feeling safe.

What things make your safety switch flip?

Who helps you when it does?

What do you like to do
to keep calm and safe?